THE GEOLOGIC STORY
OF YOSEMITE VALLEY

THE GEOLOGIC STORY
OF YOSEMITE VALLEY

By N. King Huber

In the footsteps of François E. Matthes

J. Missouri
St. Louis
MMXIV

Photo Credits: figure 2 by King of Hearts; figure 5 by Glenn Scofield Williams; figure 7 by David Iliff; figure 8 by Joe Reidhead; and figure 9 by Tuxyso. Photos are licensed under CC-BY-SA 3.0.

Cover: Photo by Matthew Roth. Licensed under CC-BY-SA 3.0.

ISBN 978-1-940777-22-1

J. Missouri
www.jmissouri.com
Saint Louis, Missouri

This book is set in Minion Pro, designed by Robert Slimbach for Adobe Systems. It was inspired by the elegant and highly readable typefaces of the late Renaissance.

Contents

YOSEMITE COUNTRY

For its towering cliffs, spectacular waterfalls, granite domes and spires, glacially-sculpted and polished rock, and beautiful alpine scenery, Yosemite National Park is world famous. Nowhere else are all these exceptional features so well displayed and so easily accessible. Artists, writers, tourists, and geologists flock to Yosemite – and marvel at its natural wonders. Yosemite Valley itself is deeply carved into the gently sloping western flank of the Sierra Nevada, the longest, the highest, and the grandest single mountain range in the United States outside of Alaska. And although other valleys with similarities exist, there is but one Yosemite Valley, the "Incomparable Valley" of John Muir, California's most famous naturalist.

FIG. 1 BIRD'S EYE VIEW of Yosemite Valley
and the High Sierra beyond.

RF	Ribbon Falls	L	Mount Lyell
EC	El Capitan	LY	Little Yosemite
EP	Eagle Peak	LC	Liberty Cap
YF	Yosemite Falls	B	Mount Broderick
R	Royal Arches	G	Glacier Point
W	Washington Column	SD	Sentinel Dome
M	Mirror Lake	SR	Sentinel Rock
TC	Tenaya Canyon	CS	Cathedral Spires
ND	North Dome	CR	Cathedral Rocks
BD	Basket Dome	BV	Bridal Veil Falls
MW	Mount Watkins	LT	Leaning Tower
C	Clouds Rest	YV	Yosemite Village
HD	Half Dome	MR	Merced River

A SCENE OF WORLDWIDE FAME

Simply stated, Yosemite Valley, only 7 miles long and nearly 1 mile wide, is a flat-floored, widened part of the canyon of the Merced River. But this broad rock-hewn trough with roughly parallel sides, is boldly sculptured and ornamented with silvery cataracts. From the valley floor at an elevation of 4,000 feet, the magnificent cliffs rise 3,000 to 4,000 feet higher to forested uplands on either side (fig. 1).

Once you enter Yosemite Valley its grandeur is overwhelming. Looking eastward up the valley from its lower end you are struck by the immensity of the sheer profile of El Capitan, the most majestic cliff in the valley (fig. 2). Projecting boldly from the north wall, its top rises 3,000 feet above the valley floor. Directly opposite stand the Cathedral Rocks, over 2,500 feet high, which also jut into the valley. Between the west end of this promontory and the Leaning Tower, Bridalveil Fall leaps 620 feet, its abundant spray commonly suffused with rainbows (fig. 3).

Eastward beyond the narrows at El Capitan and Cathedral Rocks, the valley abruptly widens, and in an embayment on the south are the Cathedral Spires, among the frailest rock shafts in the valley (fig. 4). On the north are the Three Brothers (fig. 5), whose gabled summits rise one above another, all built architecturally on the same angle. The highest, known as Eagle Peak, rises nearly 3,800 feet above the valley floor. Across the valley stands Sentinel Rock, a finely modeled obelisk with a pointed top (fig. 6).

A mile farther up the valley, on the north side, are Yosemite Falls, dramatically booming among clouds of mist during the spring and early summer snowmelt (fig. 7). The Upper Fall, 1,430 feet high, would alone make any valley famous; it is the highest unbroken leap of water on the continent. The Lower

Figure 2 - El Capitan's bold profile faces Cathedral Rocks on the right.

Figure 3 - Leaning Tower and the west flank of Cathedral Rocks frame Bridalveil.

FIGURE 4 - THE CATHEDRAL SPIRES project skyward to the left of Cathedral Rocks.

FIGURE 5 - THE THREE BROTHERS, whose angled summits slope westward.

Figure 6 - Sentinel Rock's Pinnacle juts boldly upward.

FIGURE 7 - UPPER YOSEMITE FALL now leaps from the hanging valley of Yosemite Creek. In the not-too-distant geologic past its water cascaded down through the prominent ravine to the left. The spire of Lost Arrow is visible upward and to the right of Upper Yosemite Fall.

Fall, which descends 320 feet, seems insignificant by comparison, yet it is twice as high as Niagara Falls. The entire chain of falls and intermediate cascades drops 2,425 feet. Ribbon Fall, west of El Capitan, descends 1,612 feet, but it is confined in a sheer-walled recess and does not make a clear leap throughout.

Farther up the valley, on the north side, are the Royal Arches, sculptured one within another into an inclined rock wall that rises 1,500 feet (fig. 8). An enormous natural pillar, the Washington Column, flanks them on the right, and above them rises a smoothly curving, helmet-shaped knob of granite called North Dome. Facing the Royal Arches on the south wall, stands Glacier Point providing a matchless view of the valley from its summit, which stands 3,200 feet above the valley floor.

At the head of the valley, as if on a pedestal, stands Half Dome, the most colossal and recognizable rock monument in the Sierra Nevada, smoothly rounded on three sides and a sheer vertical face on the fourth (fig. 9). From its summit, over 4,800 feet above the valley, you look southeast into Little Yosemite Valley, which is broad floored and has granite walls more gently sloping than in its larger namesake. From Little Yosemite's western portal, guarded by Liberty Cap, the Merced River descends by a giant stairway, making two magnificent waterfalls, Nevada Fall, dropping 594 feet, and Vernal Fall, dropping 317 feet. Looking northward from Half Dome's summit, the view is into Tenaya Canyon, a chasm as profound as Yosemite Valley itself, yet the pathway of only a small brook. To the northeast, Clouds Rest, the loftiest summit in the vicinity of Yosemite Valley, rises to 9,926 feet; beyond, spreads the vast panorama of the High Sierra.

The present Yosemite Valley is the result of many different geologic processes operating over an incomprehensible

FIGURE 8 - THE ROYAL ARCHES are flanked by Washington Column and surmounted by North Dome.

length of time measured in millions of years. These processes are by themselves not unique, but their unrivaled interaction has created this "Incomparable Valley." The accumulated observations, studies, and interpretations by many individuals through the years allow us to reconstruct much of the valley's geologic history, adding to our appreciation of its scenic majesty.

ROCK, THE SCULPTOR'S MEDIUM

For any form of sculpture, whether of finely-chiseled statues or massive landforms, the resulting product is strongly dependent on the nature of the material being worked upon. For Yosemite Valley that material is granite. Indeed, granite forms the bedrock of much of the Sierra Nevada, including most of Yosemite National Park. Granite, in the broad sense of the term *(granitic rock)*, is a rock with a salt-and-pepper appearance due to random distribution of light and dark minerals. The mineral grains are generally coarse enough to be individually visible to the naked eye.

Throughout the park granitic rock varies considerably in the relative proportions of the individual light and dark minerals, and these compositional differences are represented by a variety of specific names, such as granodiorite and tonalite, in addition to "true" granite as defined by geologists.

From a distance, all of Yosemite Valley's granitic rock looks the same. But it actually consists of individual rock bodies, each with their own characteristic mineral composition and texture, that is, the coarseness of their crystals and uniformity or variation in grain size. All of these variations, in turn, affect the rock's resistance to abrasion, fracturing, and weathering, all important to the sculptor and the end product. The imposing cliffs of El Capitan and Cathedral Rocks, for

Figure 9 - Half Dome's cleaved face dominates the east end of Yosemite Valley.

example, are composed of a particularly tough and resistant variety of granitic rock.

THE ROLE OF JOINTS

The bedrock structures having the greatest effects on Yosemite's landform development are joints. Although granitic rock is unbroken on a small scale, on a larger scale the rock is broken by *joints*, which are more or less planar cracks commonly found as sets of parallel fractures in the rock. Regional-scale joints commonly determine the orientation of major features of the landscape, such as the planar face of Half Dome, the series of parallel cliffs at Cathedral Rocks, and the westward sloping faces of the Three Brothers. In contrast, smaller, outcrop-scale joints determine the ease with which rock breaks and erodes. Joints are of overwhelming influence on landform development in granitic terrain because they form greatly contrasting zones of weakness in otherwise homogenous, erosion-resistant rock and allow access for water and air to enter and aid in the weathering and disintegration of rock.

The type of jointing that most influences the form of Yosemite's landmarks, however, is the broad, onion-shell-like *sheet jointing* formed by a process referred to as *exfoliation*. Granitic rocks originate at considerable depth within the Earth while under great pressure from overlying rock that may be miles thick. As the overlying rock erodes away, the decrease in the pressure that once confined the granitic rock causes it to expand toward the Earth's surface. When the outer expanding zone exceeds the strength of the rock, it cracks away from less expanded rock beneath and bursts loose as a sheet; subsequent cracks release successive layers of expanding rock. Because the expansion that forms these sheets takes place perpendicular to the local surface, the shape of sheets generally reflects topography, with curved surfaces following hill and valley. Sheet joints also tend to parallel the walls of canyons and cliffs that may appear to be unbroken monoliths, such as El Capitan, but which may have fractures behind and parallel to the cliff face. The curved upper surfaces of North Dome and Half Dome, and the undulating surface of Clouds Rest, are magnificent examples of sheet joints or sheeting (figs. 8, 9).

Admiring Yosemite Valley's intricately sculptured walls as they appear today and knowing something about the granitic rock from which they were carved, we can look back in time to speculate on the evolution of the valley's formation – its geologic history.

A STORY THAT BEGAN
MILLIONS OF YEARS AGO

The last touches to Yosemite Valley's architecture were applied relatively recently, geologically speaking. But the rock from which the valley is carved originated mainly during the Cretaceous period, about 100 million years ago, when dinosaurs roamed the Earth. At that time molten rock, *magma*, generated deep within the Earth, rose upward within the Earth's crust, or upper layer, and crystallized far beneath the surface to form granitic rock along a linear belt that was to become the future Sierra Nevada. The granitic terrain that makes up the Sierra, once thought to have only local variations in one huge mass of rock, is actually made up of a mosaic of individual rock bodies that formed from repeated intrusions of magma over many millions of years.

Some of the magma broke through to the surface, building a string of volcanoes atop hidden granitic roots, and we can perhaps envision an ancient majestic mountain range some-what like the modern Cascade Range along the coast of our Pacific Northwest. Because of the high elevation of this ances-tral range, however, the volcanic and other rocks covering the granite were soon eroded away, and by Late Cretaceous time, about 70 million years ago, the granitic rocks became exposed at the Earth's surface. By middle Cenozoic time, a few tens of millions of years ago, so much of the upper part had been removed that in the vicinity of Yosemite the surface of the range had a low relief of only a few thousand feet.

Later, the continental crust east of the Sierra Nevada began to stretch in an east-west direction, developing into a series of north-south-trending valleys and mountain ranges. Through a combination of uplift of the Sierran block and down-drop-ping of the area to the east, the Yosemite region acquired a tilted-block aspect with a long, gentle slope westward to the Central Valley of California and a short, steep slope separat-ing it from the country to the east.

AGENTS OF EROSION

Erosion, simply stated, is the removal of earth materials from high areas to lower areas, modifying the landscape in the process. Two agents of erosion are chiefly responsible for sculpting the present Yosemite landscape – flowing water and glacial ice: flowing water had the major role, and gla-cial ice added additional touches. The general Sierran land-forms were all well-established before glaciation, and the major stream drainage's provided the avenues along which the glaciers would later follow. Some of the glacial modi-fications, however, were profound: the creation of alpine topography in the High Sierra, the rounding of many valleys from V-shape to U-shape, and the straightening of valleys in the process. Still another agent of erosion is simply gravity. The downslope movement of rock materials produces landslides and rockfalls. Although generally of local extent, such movement is important, particularly in mountainous terrain and on the over-steepened slopes in Yosemite Valley.

THE ROLE OF FLOWING WATER

The effectiveness of erosion by flowing water depends both on processes of weathering – the breakdown of larger rocks into smaller individual rock and mineral fragments that can be transported – and on stream volume and velocity, which determines the size and amount of material that can be transported. With the increasing late Cenozoic elevation of the Yosemite region, the major streams coursing down its western slope were rejuvenated and made more vigorous by their increased slopes. Under these conditions the major streams cut canyons whose channels became progressively deepened relative to the upland areas between them, areas which even today retain comparatively moderate relief. The upper basins and middle reaches of the Merced and Tuolumne Rivers, for example, were later modified by glacial erosion, but initial canyon cutting was accomplished solely by the action of streams. Two sketches depict an artist's conception of the evolution of the Merced River canyon at the site of the future Yosemite Valley before the onset of glaciation (fig. 10).

THE ROLE OF GLACIERS

The Yosemite landscape as we see it today strongly reflects the dynamic influence of flowing ice that long ago covered much of its higher regions. Geologists are still uncertain how many times ice mantled Yosemite, but at least three major

Figure 10 - The role of flowing water. A few tens-of-millions of years ago the Yosemite area was a rolling surface of rounded hills and broad valleys with meandering streams (A, above). Before the onset of glaciation, more than a million years ago, the elevation of the range increased and streams incised deep canyons into the western flank of the range (B, right).

Figure 10 - The role of flowing water.

glaciations have been well documented elsewhere in the Sierra Nevada. In the higher country, icefields covered extensive areas, except for the higher ridges and peaks. Lower down the western slope, at middle elevations, glacial tongues were confined to pre-existing river canyons, such as those of the Merced and Tuolumne Rivers. Thus our focus will be on the nature and activities of these valley glaciers, particularly as they apply to Yosemite Valley, and Hetch Hetchy Valley some 15 miles to the north, but remembering that the valley glaciers derive their flowing ice from icefields higher in the range.

In contrast to the sinuous V-shaped valleys of normal streams in unglaciated mountainous terrain, glaciated valleys tend to be straighter and have U-shaped profiles. Whereas a stream erodes the outsides of bends preferentially and makes its course more sinuous, glacial erosive force is concentrated on the insides of bends, removing the protruding spurs of the original stream valley and leaving a wider, straighter valley.

The resulting modification, in detail, depends on the nature and structural integrity of the bedrock over which the glacier is flowing. For granitic bedrock, the dominant structure of concern is jointing, which controls the ease of removal of rock that is otherwise highly resistant to glacial erosion.

YOSEMITE VALLEY AND ITS GLACIERS

Yosemite Valley has often been referred to as a "classic" glacial valley. But what glacially-derived attributes does it display to deserve that designation? A glacier tends to straighten a valley and smooth its walls as it grinds past them. But the walls of Yosemite Valley are extremely ragged, with many pinnacles and spires projecting upward from them – Leaning Tower, Cathedral Spires, Sentinel Rock, and Lost Arrow stand out strikingly. All of the waterfalls and lesser cascades along the sides of the valley are ensconced in alcoves, except for Upper Yosemite Fall, whose story will be told in upcoming paragraphs. Eagle Creek and Indian Canyon Creek actually issue from deep ravines. All of these seemingly anomalous features would doubtless be obliterated by a glacier that filled the valley to its brim. And yet glacial erratics – boulders transported and deposited by a glacier – are found scattered above the valley's rim telling us that a glacier indeed once filled the valley to its brim. How can we explain this anomalous appearance if the valley was indeed shaped by a glacier? The anomaly is even more apparent if we compare Yosemite Valley with another "glaciated" valley of about the same size and elevation, Hetch Hetchy Valley, which has comparatively smooth walls and an absence of pinnacles and spires (fig. 11).

Little doubt exists that Yosemite Valley indeed represents a profound, glacially-driven modification of the Merced River canyon, as no other erosive agent could have accomplished such excavation. A glacier filling the valley to its rim created the basic broad shape of the valley and gouged out a deep bedrock basin whose bottom locally, in its eastern part, lies more than 1,000 feet below the present valley floor (fig. 12). That glacial episode was named the El Portal glaciation by François Matthes in his monumental Yosemite study, because he thought that its glacier advanced down the Merced canyon to near the community of El Portal, some 10 miles downstream from Yosemite Valley proper. Today we correlate that glaciation with the Sherwin glaciation, defined from studies along the east side of the Sierra Nevada, and which name is now in general use. The Sherwin was the most extensive, and longest-lived, glaciation documented in the Sierra. It may have lasted almost 300 thousand years and ended about 1 million years ago. A Sherwin-age glacier was

FIGURE 11 - THE HETCH HETCHY before damning. Note the absence of Yosemite-like pinnacles.

almost surely responsible for the major excavation and shaping of Yosemite Valley within the Merced River canyon.

Later glaciations in the Sierra Nevada were of lesser areal extent and briefer than the Sherwin. The best documented are the Tahoe and Tioga glaciations, which probably peaked about 130,000 and 20,000 years ago, respectively; together they are equivalent to Matthes' "Wisconsin" glacial stage, which he did not subdivide. The last glacier in Yosemite Valley – Tioga in age – advanced only as far as Bridalveil Meadow (fig. 12). At this location the forward movement of the glacier was balanced by the melting of ice at its front, or terminus. A "terminal" end moraine – a low ridge crossing the valley – was constructed with rock debris transported by the glacier and deposited at its terminus. The extent of the earlier Tahoe-age glacier in the valley is uncertain, but evidence elsewhere in the Sierra, suggests that it probably would have been somewhat longer than the Tioga. Nevertheless, since the original excavation of Yosemite Valley by a Sherwin-age glacier, no subsequent glacier has filled the valley to its rim, a conclusion that has important consequences for the scenery.

From its terminus at Bridalveil Meadow, the ice surface of the Tioga glacier would have sloped upward toward the east end of the valley with the ice reaching a thickness of perhaps a little over 1,000 feet at Columbia Rock west of Yosemite Falls, 1,500 feet at Washington Column, and 2,000 feet in Tenaya Canyon below Basket Dome, as reconstructed by Matthes. Thus the Tioga and similar Tahoe glaciers could do very little to further modify or smooth the walls of Yosemite Valley. Above the ice surface of those glaciers, the valley walls have had a million years to weather: joints widened, rock fractured and crumbled, and waterfalls and cascades eroded back into alcoves and ravines. Thus the pinnacles and spires that seem so anomalous for a glacial valley actually had a

FIGURE 12 - GLACIERS LARGE AND SMALL. Sketches of Yosemite Valley area, showing extent of valley-filling Sherwin glacier (A, above), and lesser extent of Tioga glacier (B, right).

FIGURE 12 - GLACIERS LARGE AND SMALL.

million years to form and, being above the level of later glaciers, remain to amaze us today. In Tenaya Canyon, Tioga ice was thicker and reached farther up the walls, smoothing them and removing irregularities; no pinnacles and spires are found there.

Hetch Hetchy Valley on the Tuolumne River, otherwise similar to Yosemite Valley, has comparatively smooth walls and an absence of pinnacles and spires (fig. 11). There the Tioga glacier was also less extensive than the Sherwin, but unlike the glacier in Yosemite Valley, the Tioga glacier filled Hetch Hetchy to the rim. Thus Hetch Hetchy Valley's walls were being scraped and debris was removed from the valley with each glaciation, including the last. The greater extent of the glacier in Hetch Hetchy can be attributed to the fact that the drainage basin of the Tuolumne River above Hetch Hetchy is more than three times as large as that of the Merced River above Yosemite Valley. As a result, the much larger icefield feeding the Tuolumne glacier was able to provide the necessary volume of ice to fill Hetch Hetchy even though the Tioga glaciation was regionally less extensive than the Sherwin. The smaller Merced icefield was unable to provide sufficient ice to fill Yosemite Valley, even though supplemented by ice from a part of the Tuolumne drainage that flowed southwest over a low pass into Tenaya Canyon.

LEAPING FALLS AND HANGING VALLEYS

Waterfalls leaping out from a valley's walls far above the valley floor have long been considered evidence of a glacial origin for the valley. The enormous Sherwin-age glacier that shaped Yosemite Valley was able to excavate the central chasm to a greater depth than smaller glaciers in side-entering tributaries. The result was that some of the side valleys were left "hanging" with waterfalls at their brinks. Since Sherwin time, most of the tributaries have eroded their channels back into the walls to leave little more than steep ravines with minor falls interrupted by chains of cascades, such as those at Sentinel Fall. Bridalveil Fall is an exception, although it also has receded back into an alcove from its original position further out on the valley wall.

In contrast to Bridalveil Fall, Upper Yosemite Fall, although leaping from a hanging valley, had a very different origin. Yosemite Creek is the largest stream flowing into the north side of Yosemite Valley and probably entered the Merced River canyon through a steep side canyon before glaciation. After the Sherwin glacier deepened Yosemite Valley, Yosemite Creek continued to enter the main valley through that ravine, which lies just to the west of the present falls (fig. 7). Matthes recognized this and described "what appears to be an old stream channel leading just to the west of the present channel." At that time the site of the present Upper Fall hosted only a minor ephemeral fall of short duration during spring runoff.

Matthes did not speculate on how or when Yosemite Creek was diverted from that old channel into its present channel to create its Upper Fall. He did, however, map a morainal complex that he attributed to his "Wisconsin-age" glacier that flowed down Yosemite Creek, but stopped about one-half mile short of the rim of Yosemite Valley itself. A plausible explanation for the diversion of Yosemite Creek into its present channel is that the stream was temporarily blocked by glacial deposits and had to find a new way through the intricate complex of nested moraines. As his Wisconsin glacial stage includes both Tahoe and Tioga glaciations, Upper Yosemite Fall, with its "newly" hanging valley, can be little more than 130,000 years old. And what a spectacular addition to Yosemite Valley's architectural wonders it is!

YOSEMITE VALLEY'S GLACIAL FINALE

While the Tioga glacier was constructing its terminal moraine at Bridalveil Meadow, the climate apparently warmed slightly. The ice at the front of the glacier began to melt faster than the ice was moving forward, and the ice front, or "snout," of the still-flowing glacier began to "retreat" up the valley. The climate cooled again; the ice front paused and temporarily stabilized just west of El Capitan Meadow. Here the glacier began to construct a new moraine, known as a "recessional" moraine because the glacier had receded from its terminal position. It remained at this location longer than it had at Bridalveil Meadow and the resultant El Capitan Moraine is larger in both volume and height. Eventually, the climate warmed abruptly, and the Merced glacier's snout retreated toward the head of the valley with no more recessional pauses, probably leaving Yosemite Valley by 15,000 years ago.

When the Tioga-age glacier departed from Yosemite Valley it left behind a lake, which Matthes christened *Lake Yosemite* (fig. 13). It is likely that the advancing Tioga glacier had excavated some of the pre-existing valley fill east of the El Capitan Moraine, creating a shallow lake basin. The lake was in part dammed by this moraine, with the Merced River flowing over a low spillway through the moraine near the south valley wall. As the separate arms of the Tioga glacier retreated up the Merced and Tenaya canyons, the meltwater-swollen, debris-laden rivers issuing from their snouts delivered large quantities of sediment to the lake basin. The lake was soon filled in with this sediment, creating the

FigURE 13 - GLACIAL LAKE YOSEMITE filled the basin left upstream from El Capitan morain after the retreat of Tioga ice from Yosemite Valley.

relatively level valley floor we see today. The resulting gentle slope allowed the Merced River to develop a sinuous meander pattern across this broad flood plain. A low-gradient, meandering stream is particularly susceptible to over-bank flow during high water, and its flood plain is naturally destined for periodic flooding.

THE ROCKS COME TUMBLING DOWN

The Tioga-age glacier did little to modify Yosemite Valley other than to remove pre-existing talus at the base of cliffs east of Bridalveil Meadow; all of the talus there now has accumulated in the last 15,000 years or so since the Tioga glacier departed. In contrast, the enormous talus slope west of El Capitan, known as the Rockslides, escaped the reach of the Tioga glacier. For the past million years, then, the rock walls of the valley that remained above the ice-level of the smaller post-Sherwin glaciers have weathered, joints have been enlarged, and rock has spalled off to form the very irregularly sculptured surface we see today. This geologic history provides the setting for abundant rockfalls. Every significant historical rockfall in Yosemite Valley has originated in vulnerable fractured rock from above the level of the Tioga glacier. Some rockfalls are quite large, but most are relatively small and gradually build up a cone of debris below the most active sites. Thus the size of a debris cone can reflect the volume or the frequency of individual falls, or a combination. The shattered rock high on the east side of Middle Brother provides material for a debris cone at one of the most active rockfall sites in the valley. Given the nature of the geologic setting, it is inevitable that such rockfalls will continue as part of ongoing geologic processes.

EPILOGUE

The geologic story of Yosemite Valley, as presented here, describes our present understanding of the interplay of various geologic processes that contributed to the valley's creation. But this is not the last word. We are still learning about these various processes and their effects on the evolution of the valley. And, indeed, these geologic processes are far from finished. We are seeing only a brief period in time in the landscape's ongoing history. Dynamic geologic processes will continue to change the many faces of this "Incomparable Valley."

OTHER TITLES

PUBLISHED BY

J. MISSOURI

Available worldwide and at www.jmissouri.com.

The Yosemite. Here is John Muir's classic guidebook to Yosemite. In passionate and vivid prose, Muir describes the geology, flora, fauna, weather, seasons, and human history of Yosemite. He provides readers with accounts of his adventures, from riding an avalanche to walking behind Yosemite Falls. Muir also lists good one to multi-day excursions for the Yosemite visitor. This J. MISSOURI edition contains 20 portraits of Yosemite and a detailed map of Yosemite Valley. Illustrated. Paperback. 188 pages.

The Story of the Yosemite Valley. François Matthes gives a tour of the great geological wonders of Yosemite Valley. In rich detail, Matthes walks readers through Yosemite Valley today. He then takes us back to the birth of the Sierra Nevada and describes the slow creation of the Valley's famed waterfalls, beautiful hanging valleys, and soaring rock walls. Illustrations of the geological process and photos of Yosemite make this short book an excellent introduction to Yosemite Valley. Illustrated. Paperback. 34 pages.

My First Summer in the Sierra. John Muir recounts his early travels in the Sierra while working as a shepherd. In the summer of 1869, Muir set out from California's Central

Valley with a flock of 2,050 sheep and made his way to the headwaters of the Merced and Tuolumne Rivers. As one of America's great philosopher naturalists, Muir captures the spirit of the Sierra Nevada and brings the reader along as a witness to his great journey. He explores in great detail the mountains, meadows, waterfalls, flora, and fauna of the rich landscape that captured his heart. My First Summer in the Sierra is an excellent introduction to the writings of John Muir. This J. MISSOURI edition contains 30 illustrations. Paperback. 182 pages.

Woodcraft and Camping. George Washington Sears, also known as "Nessmuk," was a Romantic. He sought to witness the glory and the beauty of nature; to free himself from the vagaries of industrialized civilization. He expressed this philosophy through his pursuit of the minimalist ideal and its use in the outdoors. Woodcraft and Camping is Nessmuk's practical and philosophical guide to camping, traveling, and survival in the woods. The book discusses the foundational skills needed to live in the woods: the art of camping, fishing, fire-making, cooking, shelter, tools, and canoeing. But Nessmuk does not just recite the skills needed, he also tells us about his experiences and conversations during his travels. He provides us with campfire poetry and lore. And he does all of this in a writing style that is eloquent, engrossing, and intrinsically positive. Illustrated. Paperback. 112 pages.

Shelters, Shacks and Shanties. Daniel Beard, an early leader of the Boy Scouts of America, teaches readers how to build a large variety of practical shelters using either a hatchet or an axe. There are over 50 different shelters described, including lean-tos, teepees, hogans, bark houses, a sod house, stilt houses, tree houses, one room log cabins, and large log houses. 332 illustrations that detail the construction of the shelters make this an excellent book for all ages. Paperback. 240 pages.

The Compleat Angler. Izaak Walton's fishing classic is a celebration of the art and spirit of fishing. Through prose, verse, song, and folklore, Walton inspires readers to go into nature—to go to its meandering streams and rivers—and fish. Walton teaches us about a life filled with harmony between nature, man, and God; and a life spent in the company of friends and free from the hustle of the city. Illustrated. Paperback. 186 pages.

Walking. In his classic essay on Walking, Henry David Thoreau, the famous naturalist and philosopher, extols the virtues of immersing ourselves daily in nature. Thoreau treats the act of walking as a vehicle that transports us to the sacred space that is nature. The wildness of nature becomes a retreat from the noise of contemporary society and civilization—a place to rest our thoughts and regain balance between these two worlds. This J. MISSOURI edition contains nearly 40 new historical and biographical footnotes. Paperback. 48 pages.

Nature. In this classic essay, Ralph Waldo Emerson presents the foundations of Transcendentalism, the belief system in which the divine permeates nature and in which reality is understood through nature. Paperback. 72 pages.

Caves of Missouri. In this reprint of a classic piece of cave literature, the famed geologist, J Harlen Bretz, gives a detailed account of the formation and history of Missouri caves. Caves of Missouri contains over 450 surveyed caves, with in-depth geological and cultural histories, and 168 illustrations, including cross sections, maps, and photographs. This book is an excellent resource for anyone interested in Missouri's natural and cultural history. Paperback. 582 pages.

Granite Climbs of Missouri. Granite Climbs of Missouri is the most extensive guidebook to the rock climbing routes and bouldering problems of Missouri's granite heartland—the St. Francois Mountains. Only an hour and a half south of St. Louis, the Silver Mines, Millstream Gardens, and Amidon offer some of the best climbing in Missouri. The book contains over 420 documented routes, and over 275 of these are easy to moderate in difficulty. Color photos and maps help climbers locate routes with ease and speed. Paperback. 212 pages.

Cave Explorations in Missouri, Indiana, Illinois, Kentucky, Tennessee, and Alabama. Gerard Fowke, the famed American archaeologist and geologist, gives detailed accounts of the archaeological and geological histories of more than 180 caves throughout the American Midwest and South. Through in-depth descriptions and over 90 illustrations, Fowke provides readers with a look into the formation of these caves and the early people who inhabited them. Paperback. 230 pages.

The Ascent of Denali: Annotated Edition. Hudson Stuck recounts his successful expedition to climb Denali (officially Mount McKinley) for the first time. Though the small, independent expedition faced many challenges and setbacks—many of their supplies were destroyed in a fire, they climbed in moccasins, and they used locally made ice axes—the team reached the summit of Denali without any loss of life or significant injuries. In addition to documenting the journey, Stuck also provides readers with a history of the ascents attempted before the 1913 expedition. Also included are 34 photographs and illustrations, including Stuck's original map of the mountain. This J. Missouri edition contains 40 new historical and biographical footnotes. Also included is a glossary of some of the early named features on and around Denali. Paperback. 162 pages.

Rock Climbs of Johnson Shut-Ins State Park. This is the dedicated guidebook to one of Missouri's most beautiful and historic climbing areas. This book contains 67 documented top rope and traditional routes, reaching heights of almost 60 feet. Johnson Shut-Ins is an excellent area for both first-timers, with its easy access and beginner routes, and experienced leaders, with many hard and thin traditional routes. This book features color photos, a glossary of terms for new climbers, and a brief geological and climber history of Johnson Shut-Ins. 48 pages.

Printed in Great Britain
by Amazon